XF
Goennel, Heidi
    If I were a penguin.

EAST

COPY 1

$14.45

If I Were a Penguin . . .

If I Were a Penguin...

Heidi Goennel

Little, Brown and Company

Boston   Toronto   London

First edition

Library of Congress Cataloging-in-Publication Data
Goennel, Heidi.
  If I were a penguin . . .
  Summary: A child imagines the fun of being different animals, such as an eagle, a camel, and a giraffe.
  1. Animals — Miscellanea — Juvenile literature.
[1. Animals — Miscellanea] I. Title.
QL49.G58 1989   591   88-8327
ISBN 0-316-31841-8

10 9 8 7 6 5 4 3 2 1
NIL
Published simultaneously in Canada
by Little, Brown & Company (Canada) Limited

Printed in Italy

To Peter

If I weren't me, what could I be?
If I were a penguin ...

I could swim in the winter.

If I were a frog

I could live in a pond.

If I were a camel

I could walk across the desert.

If I were a mouse

I could fit in tiny places.

If I were a fish

I could swim across the ocean.

If I were a turtle

I could carry my house on my back.

If I were a rabbit

I could hop across the lawn.

If I were a monkey

I could swing in the vines.

If I were a pig

I could play in the mud.

If I were a horse

I could gallop across the meadow.

If I were an eagle

I could soar way up high.

If I were a mole

I could travel underground.

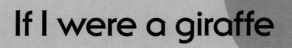

If I were a giraffe

I could see the tops of trees.

But mostly I'm happy to be just me.